MW00627579

ISBN: 978-0-578-98344-8

Rose of Jericho Meaning (on the cover):

When I was researching design for the cover, I was led to this plant. My initial thought was, "but it's so ugly," and then I quickly was convicted of that thought and I immediately realized, so are our situations. Let me explain: The Rose of Jericho is not the most glamorous flower, but it is a plant that we as survivors of toxic relationships can relate to.

My main point is that the Rose of Jericho is an herb known for its ability to come back to life after appearing to dry out and die. Read that again, did you catch that? The situations we encounter in life can be deceiving and make us feel like we can't come back from the pain of a toxic situation. But, that is a lie, and like the Rose of Jericho, things aren't always what they seem. We as women, as God's daughters, like the Rose of Jericho, have the super power and that power is the ability to revive ourselves after situations that are meant to steal our peace, our lives, and our purpose.

DEDICATION

This journal is dedicated to all the women who have endured a toxic, unhealthy relationship or marriage and lost their life at the hands of the person who they thought loved them. I hope this tool inspires women who feel stuck in chaos to find the strength to be strong and live again. **Unapologetically**. This book is also dedicated to my daughter, Heaven. I teach you daily how to love and be loved and I pray you pass that love onto others. You are a bright light and I love you.

Table of Contents

FOREWARD

There's a certain glow that comes with fully dedicating your life to pursuing your purpose and allowing God to lead your steps — and Destiny has that glow, undeniably. From the moment I met her, she has radiated this bright light of hope, joy, and love. She has the kind of spirit that you are drawn to. That spirit is also the spirit of a woman who has been through the wringer and learned to truly trust God with everything in her.

As I read and worked through this journal, I found myself releasing some much-needed bitterness that I too was holding onto from past toxic relationships. In "Inspired to Live Again: Guided Journal," Destiny is raw, vulnerable, and real. She exposes the myths of love and the truths of Christ. She provokes you to tap into the hidden memories that we all have fearfully trapped within our minds.

Over the years of our amazing friendship, I have watched Destiny open up and become vulnerable in the most graceful and admirable way. She has removed the guilt, shame, and fear of being judged by man and has allowed her test to truly become her testimony.

So while you go on this journey of self-healing, I pray over each and every one of you. I pray that you all are willing and able to fully let go and let God. Leave your hurt, pain, shame, or guilt in this journal and at the foot of the cross.

May God bless you, keep you, and propel you forward.

With love xoxo

Rev. Telissa Espie

IG:@HeyTelissa

PRAYER

Most of us spend a considerable portion of our adult lives trying to come to terms with what has happened to us in the past. Our prayers, our repentance, and our desires all seem to focus on what life would be like if only that incident hadn't happened, or if only that gaping emotional wound in our heart could be healed once and for all. But this kind of living must come to an end. If we truly desire a serious and continuous growth in our walk with the Lord, we must realize that dragging around all that stuff from our past eventually becomes too much to bear, too much to keep track of, and definitely too much to fit into God's plan for our lives. I understand. The pain has been too hard for too long. We know better. The pain is there even with a cover over it.

There is a place of healing in the spirit of God, and a personal reality of His presence that the Lord yearns for us to experience. He sees our pain, understands our struggle, and wants nothing more than to bring wholeness back to you.

As I write this prayer to you, my heart is rejoicing because I know you will find healing from the trauma, abandonment, rejection, victimization, isolation, pride, and many other wounds within your soul. I have ministered to women in the area of inner healing and freedom in Christ and they have experienced immediate transformation from saying **The PRAYER of UNFORGIVENESS. This is the prayer that set me on the path to freedom once and for all.**

If you truly want to experience wholeness, allow the Holy Spirit to search your heart NOW. List anyone whom you need to forgive **from your heart**. Start with the top three people you need to forgive. Repeat this prayer from your heart and with your "I mean it" voice.

"Heavenly Father, I forgive (name the person) from my heart for all the things that he/she did to me. (Tell God all that they did.) I let him/her go free. I lay nothing to his/her charge. I require nothing of him/her. I release him/her into your hands, Father, for You to get vengeance as You so choose. I forgive (person's name) from my heart for all the things he/she did just because You, Heavenly Father, have already forgiven me. Now, I release blessings to him/her, Please make me a blessing to him/her in Jesus' name. Amen."

2

Say this prayer every day until you feel a release in your heart!

Love you, sis,

Yada Carey,

Founder & Director of The Uncommon Woman Inc. International Ministries, and Restored Roots Inner Healing and Deliverance Ministry

Certified Life Coach

FB: Yada Nicole

FB: Women Business Owners in Network

IG:@yada_womenentrepreneurs

A LETTER TO YOU, MY NEW FRIEND

Thank you for taking the time to invest in this journal. I am not a writer, a preacher, or qualified professional. I haven't even read the Bible the whole way through ... yet. (Don't judge me!) I am a steady work in progress. I am a single mother, actress, and woman who lost everything and still found hope to win in life. So, what qualifies me to create this tool in an effort to inspire you to live again? Well, honestly, I'm not qualified ... not if we base this on college degrees and careers. But I am called. Called to my purpose of being a solution and resource to someone else's pain. To that end, I've created this interactive tool that references my real-life experiences and circumstances to help you process what's going on in your own life. Journaling, and seeing my circumstances and situation on paper, helped me beyond belief. Simple as that. And, now, I'm glad I get to share it all with you.

This is not a step-by-step tutorial on how to leave your man. It is simply a toolkit filled with affirmations, snippets of my personal story, lessons to learn, and scriptures to meditate on. I hope it will all inspire you to make the best choice for your life's current circumstances. I created this to help you step back and take a look at your life — no longer from the perspective of your feelings, but based on your truth! I created this journal so you could pour out your feelings into its pages, remove your rose-colored glasses, and see what you are really going through. Love and infatuation can be truly blinding. But let's be honest: If it is truly love you are experiencing, then you wouldn't be reading this. Because *love is a lot of things, but toxic isn't one of them.*

-Destiny W.

1 Corinthians 13: 4-6 (NIV) "Love is patient, love is kind. It does not envy, it does not boast, it is not proud. It does not dishonor others, it is not self-seeking, it is not easily angered, it keeps no record of wrongs. Love does not delight in evil but rejoices with the truth."

This Journal **is** for:

- The woman who has tried, or is trying, everything to save her marriage/relationship to no avail but realizes something toxic is in the air and is ready to confront her truth.
- The woman who knows it is time to walk away and save herself from the toxicity she has been exposed to.
- The woman who is ready to Fully Live Again and leave all the toxicity and enabling behind.

Let's make one thing very clear. In no way am I advocating that women leave their marriage. Marriage is sacred and I believe you truly know in your heart if leaving is on the table as an option. With that said, as we navigate your life and heart, opening old wounds and recognizing new ones, I suggest keeping this journal easily accessible for those moments when you need to be motivated or inspired or need to jot down your thoughts. To be inspired to live again after a toxic relationship, you first need to *uncover your truths,* see your life for what it truly is, right now at this moment, and accept it. Once you do that, you'll more easily see that God never meant for you to settle, but instead He created you to live abundantly, even when you are going through your darkest and most painful times.

GUIDED JOURNAL INSTRUCTIONS

Congratulations, you're ready to begin your self-reflective journey. In this journal, we will navigate your heart, thoughts, and relationships. Along the way, journal prompts and activities will aid you in digging deeper to find your truth. When writing down your feelings and answers, operate in honesty to allow complete vulnerability. Everything in this journal will help to separate you from your emotions so you can truly analyze the truth of your current relationship and inner thoughts. To balance out the painful truths and memories, you will also find positive words affirming your value and scriptures from God's Word to meditate on. You got this! Let's begin your journey.

John 8:32 (NLT): "And you will know the truth, and the truth will set you free."

1 RED FLAGS

Warning always comes before destruction. I'm willing to bet that 90% of all negative experiences we've encountered were preceded by an inkling or red flag that we sadly ignored, myself included. And I take 100% accountability for that, because the red flags in my situation were waving as loud and proud as a train's horn. But I purposely ignored them. All decisions lead to consequences, some of which I still have to live with today.

Let's look at a few obvious and discreet toxic relationship red flags to help wrap your brain around the seriousness of toxic situations and prepare you to accept your truth and discover, or in some cases confirm, if you are in fact in a toxic relationship.

TIME TO BE HONEST: ARE YOU IN A TOXIC RELATIONSHIP?

[Place a check next to each statement you have experienced or can relate to]

Take your time and think about each of these red flags. Do they sound familiar? Be honest and mark each red flag you've experienced.

Is your partner:

- unreliable or inconsistent
- spiteful
- controlling
- always negative
- draining to be around
- disrespectful
- easily angered
- abusive, emotionally and/or physically
- possessive
- drama-fueled
- defensive all the time

Does your partner:

- hold grudges
- hate being wrong
- not want to grow
- keep a scorecard
- give you the silent treatment
- never want anyone else around, just the two of you
- never keep his word
- never reciprocate (takes but doesn't give)
- never let you forget what you did wrong
- blame you for his problems
- justify the things he does that are wrong
- sweep issues under the rug and would rather forget they are there
- gaslight you
- cross boundaries you've set
- have a sense of entitlement
- direct all roads back to him, in conversation
- say it was a joke after saying something hurtful
- run hot and cold, one minute loving you and showering you with gifts and adoration then suddenly seeming to hate you
- want you to prioritize him and his needs
- become a different person around others
- dismiss your feelings and kind gestures
- say he's sorry without any changes in action

Do you feel like:

- you aren't good enough
- you are the only one trying
- you have to walk on eggshells
- you are always in a constant state of chaos and confusion
- you are being manipulated
- you are convenient for him and often an option and not a

priority
- you are giving your all and still it's not enough
- you have developed health issues or panic attacks since you've been with him
- you are scared for your life when you are with him
- you need to involve the authorities

Narcissist

nar-cis-sist | noun

A person who has an excessive interest in or admiration of themselves

Doesn't sound that bad, does it? Not at first anyway. But it's not a risk I recommend you take. A narcissist's goal is to validate their ego. So if that means breaking you down, instilling fear, and obtaining complete control of you to attain that, then so be it. They can start off very charming and then turn on you. If you're not aware of a narcissist's traits, they can drag you right down their rabbit hole of pain and chaos. I wasn't aware that narcissistic people existed, nor did I know of toxicity. When I discovered that there was a name for the person I was dealing with, I was shocked and excited at the same time, because now I knew I wasn't crazy and the type of person he was had a name. You too may be shocked to notice some of the familiar traits of a narcissist.

Have you seen any of these traits in your relationship?

He is:

- full of himself and talks himself up
- in constant need of praise
- panicky or aggressive when you want to break up
- lacking in empathy
- often depressed

If you checked any of these boxes, then you should be concerned and on alert. You're likely in a toxic relationship. You have some reflecting to do and decisions to make. But we will get to that.

First, let me share my story with you. Please let it resonate with you. I truly believe I endured that dark season just for you — yes, the beautiful woman who is reading this right now. This is your wake-up call. God strategically organized this moment to allow you to open your eyes and to use my toxic experience to remind you that you have a choice. A choice not to settle, a choice to live a better, more full life, surrounded by love and joy. There is absolutely nothing you have ever done that obligates you to a life filled with daily pain, whether verbally, emotionally, and especially not physically.

Proverbs 16:18 (NIV): "Pride goes before destruction, a haughty spirit before a fall."

2 MY STORY:

EVERYTHING I NEVER WANTED

It all started in the summer of '97 when I was 12. I was walking down Southlawn Drive in New Orleans and I met him. The little Native American-looking boy with the curly hair who would soon become my first love, father of my child, and eventually my husband. I didn't like him (at least that's what I let him think). We grew to be good friends. I would help him make handmade cards for his mom and we'd hang out regularly. We lived around the corner from each other, so we were sure to run into each other daily. The bond that formed was very innocent and I grew to realize that he was a sweet boy who had a major crush on me. This went on until I left New Orleans in 2000, in the middle of my 10th grade year. We kept in touch over those years as pen pals and with rare phone calls. Eventually, we lost touch.

As fate would have it, at age 19 when I was graduating high school in San Diego, we would reunite. If I'm honest, I went searching for someone to love me. I was having major issues at home and I was feeling alone, so I guess I remembered someone who at one point had love for me. I reached out to a mutual friend who I knew still kept in touch with his family and asked her for his number. I held on to the number for a few days and then one evening I dialed his number. I was extremely nervous, would he even remember me?

He answered the phone and my heart sank. Who was this deep voice on the other end? "Hello," I said, and he asked who I was. "Destiny … Do you remember me?" He did, and we grew silent for a moment that felt like forever. "Damn, for real," he finally said, breaking the silence. From that moment, we spoke daily. He filled my voids and gave me the time I felt that I needed. I grew more attracted to him daily, not even physically because he lived in Georgia and I was in Dallas. I was attracted to his kindness, how gentle he was with me and the effort he put forth. Back then, my favorite show was "CSI," I mean everyone knew not to call or attempt to talk to me when this show was on. On days that I couldn't watch, he would stay home and watch it for me so he could call me and fill me in on what I missed.

Eventually, we met in person. I flew to Atlanta and I didn't want to leave. He would always ask me to come and visit, never offering to come to me. (Red flag.) But I didn't care. I was falling in love. Eventually, he came to visit a few times. The more comfortable we became with each other, I noticed he would get mad easily and yell (another red flag), but I dismissed it. Everyone gets angry sometimes, right? After all, he was still so sweet and kind and gave me all the attention that I craved. I justified any time he would get angry, yell, or become overly jealous (red flag) when we were together. This was my first real relationship and I considered his actions normal even when I didn't feel in my heart it was. We were two totally different people: He ran the street and I was a good girl from the suburbs. Never mind that we didn't look like we fit each other. I loved him and he loved me.

What happened over the next 20 years has shaped, molded, and created me to be who I am today. I was cheated on, lied to, had a miscarriage in 2006, and was in an on-and-off relationship with him. On his trip down to Dallas, in April 2008, my daughter was conceived and in June I found out that I was pregnant with our child. I was scared, I wasn't ready, and I definitely know he wasn't. By this time, he was disrespectful to me regularly and we argued all the time (red flag). And still, I had no sense of responsibility when he was around, my all was rooted in him. Then, in 2015, I filed for bankruptcy, married him, sacrificed my good job for what I thought was love and to have my family, and moved to Atlanta — all in the same year. Yes, I disregarded all of the pain he put me through, took him back as I often did, and still married him.

We moved into a nice townhome in the city of Palmetto, right outside of Atlanta. It was perfect, I had what I wanted, my family — him, Heaven, and me. Even though we were finally all together, life still happened. I tried to find a job to no avail and was unemployed until fall of 2016. Because my husband at the time was being difficult and wouldn't pay my car note and complained about taking care of us and paying the rent, I in 30 days put together a curriculum, registered a business, and secured a contract with a local church to teach a kids summer acting class. Talk about turning something into nothing. I made $5,000, but that didn't last long. I was in no way focused and for the life of me, at that time, I could not figure out why I was not enjoying something I loved to do almost as much as performing.

The thing is, I did know I was just justifying his actions as I normally did. Up to this point, he was complaining about us being there, about him having to provide for his family. Because he was overwhelmed and felt like I brought nothing to the table, I believe he began to look at me differently, like I was beneath him. He began to verbally abuse me, telling me to go back to Texas and telling me that he hated me. As the pressure for him to provide intensified, he made sure to mask the pressure with pills and weed so that he was high all the time. Rent was almost always behind, I often had to ask my parents for money to cover bills.

One night, he came home high as usual and his frustration with me not working mixed with the gall of me asking him to pick up our first-grader from the bus stop that afternoon while I went on a job interview had pissed him off to the highest level. He arrived home around 7 p.m. He didn't pick up our daughter and I missed my interview. And he was on a warpath. He dug in to me by telling me how much he hated me and asked why I was even still there in Georgia. I was confused. He told me that he hated me and told me to take my ass back to Texas, but not before ending the sentence calling me a "broke bitch." I was mortified, how could someone who says he loves me be so hateful? I cried and left the house once Heaven was asleep. I drove to the local Sonic, parked in a stall, and cried more. Eventually, I called my mom crying. She comforted me and told me to come home, but I knew I was going to stay. When I got home, it was a totally different story, He greeted me at the door like nothing had even happened! WTH? (red flag!) He was sweet, never apologized but manipulated me so well that I honestly forgot about it and went on about our night. This would become our norm, an unhealthy norm, and it was starting to affect my life internally and externally.

It felt like my life was unraveling at the seams. At the age of 21, I was diagnosed with endometriosis and now along with being diagnosed with prediabetes, my endometriosis came back with vengeance. My hair started falling out, I gained 50+ pounds putting me right under 200 pounds, depression set in, panic/anxiety attacks began, and I totally lost myself and my spirituality.

My daughter also was not herself and was a clear product of her toxic environment. At times, I would just sit on the couch and not move or speak. I felt paralyzed. I couldn't think or hold a decent conversation with an adult, if I had even had someone to talk to. The constant walking on egg-hells, plus the disrespect and fear all while trying to keep a smile on my face, was literally killing me slowly from the inside out. Pain will physically and mentally affect you and now the years of dealing were showing from the inside out. My daughter who normally was full of joy was now becoming more withdrawn and mean, but what do you expect from a child who witnessed her parents always arguing and her Dad disrespecting her mom.

Things were so bad that now sometimes I wonder, "Did it really ever happen?" But it did. Every night, I would call my parents or my sister crying. They would tell me to come home, but I couldn't. I felt I had to do everything I could to save my marriage. I prayed and fasted. I even asked my husband to seek the help he told me he would find, but he never did. The toxicity of my marriage had completely taken over my life and now I was paying for it. What did I do to deserve all of this? I played that question back over and over, daily. I was loyal, nurturing, supportive, beautiful, a good wife and mother, and I couldn't figure out why I had to pay in pain for trying to make this marriage work.

Part of the reason I agreed to move to Atlanta was that, as an actress, I was right there in the thick of it all to pursue what I felt led to do — Act. It's the Hollywood of the South, after all! But for the life of me, I couldn't book an audition, let alone find an agent. "NO" became an expected and tolerated response. Eventually, I found a part-time job working for a country club and still all hell seemed to be breaking loose.

My husband could not seem to function daily without being high on something. He was never home, always in and out of jail. Drug use and jail rotation was a regular evolution with him even before we were married. I guess, I felt like I could help him, you know? Since he had helped me through a tough time, from the day I called him when I was 19, I clearly was accepting of the minimal drug use from the beginning. Now it had spiraled out of control and I didn't even notice it. He was always the "bad boy," but that's not who I knew or loved. I loved the sweet boy from New Orleans and now I was stuck dealing with this new person and I hated it. Everything I turned a blind eye to, everything I justified, everything I allowed, every red flag I ignored from the beginning was now coming back to bite me. I was being manipulated and I was having to fight him more often. Each time he put his hands on me, I fought back; I never once cowered. Dread entered my body any time I anticipated his arrival, and I always walked on eggshells, fearing anything would spark his anger.

13

But something happened on Dec. 12, 2017. It was my life-changing moment. I was home with my daughter and her cousin around 11 p.m. My husband called, asking that I come get him, as he often did. I had become his own personal Uber. I refused because the girls were asleep and I wasn't driving 30 minutes from our house to get him. We exchanged words and he did his best to make me feel guilty but also remind me that he was pissed. I remember him telling me, "Fuck you, Bitch!" over and over and calling back to tell me how much he hated me. When I finally got enough sense to hang up, I tried my best to fall asleep. Around 1 a.m., I awoke to the sound of his key jiggling in the door. I turned over, feigning sleep. I wasn't in the mood to argue again, especially with the girls sleeping down the hall.

He came upstairs, turning on every light and throwing things around to get me up. He succeeded. I "woke up" to tell him to chill because the girls were asleep. Then I looked at him. His eyes were black and glazed over. He gritted his teeth. I knew he was high. His anger then reached an all-time high. Pause: He always had an anger problem; the drugs just elevated it. Play: As the argument began, the disrespect followed. He told me to go back to Texas, that he didn't want me around anymore (a favorite track on his toxic playlist). He called me out of my name and created havoc. It was common for him to tell me he hated me, to ask me why I was even here. He had mastered verbal abuse and killed a little bit of my spirit every time he uttered something hateful. I had had enough of the arguing. "Fine," I said, "I'll leave." That was it. I started packing my suitcase.

He had the nerve to get angry after I followed his command. He began trashing the room and throwing ALL of my stuff down the stairs. Through all of this, the girls never woke up. Thank God. I yelled, demanding he stop, and tried to gather things as he threw them down the stairs. Then, as I ascended the stairs, he pushed me. I remember being caught off guard as my face landed on the carpeted steps, wondering why he felt he needed to do that. With tears streaming down my face, I tried to shut the door on him as I ran into the room, but it wouldn't close. He had broken it in a previous altercation. He burst in and slapped me, serving me with hooks left and right. Suddenly, I was outside my own body, watching myself being hit, looking at the hate in his eyes. When he was done punching me, he began choking me. This was different from any other fight we'd had. This time, there was so much anger. I could feel the hatred. I started to fight back and pushed him into the closet. But then I stopped fighting. I just wanted it all to stop. Girl, I was tired — tired of fighting, tired of losing, tired of being a failure.

He beat me to a bloody pulp, then headed to the girls' room to wake them up, knowing this would energize me to continue the fight. And so I obliged. I grabbed his arm, and as he turned around to snatch his arm away from me, he went flying into the other room. Not sure what was going on, I trailed behind him a couple of seconds later only to meet him in the hallway coming out of our extra bedroom with his gun. There we were, standing off in the hallway. I was shirtless and only wore sweatpants. In the fight, he had torn off my shirt, bra, hair extensions, and necklace. He blocked me and the stairs as he raised the gun, pointing it between my eyes — just 2 inches stood between my face and the gun. I couldn't tell if the safety was on or not. It didn't matter.

All time stopped at that moment. Do you know how in movies, when time dramatically stops? That's what it felt like. Everything was still around me, time didn't move, he was frozen, my tears had stopped, my heart was calm and stopped racing, and I was no longer scared. I saw the black in his eyes, the anger in his face, and that I was in a standoff. Everything that had happened over the years had led to this point. I didn't think about dying, my life didn't flash before my eyes, I just felt confused. When time began again. I asked him, "Are you going to shoot me? Right now, with your daughter in the next room?" He said nothing, just stared at me. "Fine," I said. "Then shoot me."

No, I was not on a suicide mission, but I was tired of fighting and at this point it was out of my control. I had no words left. I looked toward Heaven's room and asked him again if he was going to shoot me with Heaven in the other room. After what felt like forever, he lowered the gun to his side and ran down the stairs and out of the house. He wouldn't come back until the next day. Flash forward: Upon his arrival the next day, he tried to convince me that he never pulled a gun on me. See how narcissism and gaslighting works? There was no way he could be wrong or at fault).

Back in the moment: After he fled the house, I ran into the bathroom, shut the door, and with my phone snapped a picture of my face and sent it along with a message to his younger brother and his brother's girlfriend. No response. (Neither even mentioned it when I saw them later that week.) I remember feeling guilty and embarrassed, so I actually erased the picture from my phone then got up to go to the bathroom. I looked at myself in the mirror, bloody, bruised, and scratched up. I didn't even know who I was looking at anymore. The light inside me was gone and I couldn't recognize who I was. "How did I get here, to this point," I asked myself.

Clear as day, I heard a calm, still voice inside me say, "If you stay, you will die." I began crying uncontrollably. I knew and felt that the voice didn't mean dying in the natural, but rather dying spiritually, and losing the rest of my soul. That moment, that voice, changed my life forever. At that moment, I decided to trust God and make a choice to try to leave my marriage.

I never told my family what happened that night until June 2021. But in 2019, I began sharing my testimony with other women whom God put in my path. That year, I also confronted him about the events of that night and he again insisted it never happened, but if it did, he was sorry. It wasn't until later, **in 2020,** that he finally admitted it had happened.

After that night, I spent the next two months praying, fasting, trying to take the high road, and secretly mapping out my exit plan. Once I was at peace that I was released from this marriage and could make a plan, God gave me the date of Feb. 28, 2018, as a date that I could leave. I was able to save enough money to fly my sister down from Dallas and begin to execute my exit plan. After buying her ticket, I had only $100 to my name. The Tuesday before I was set to leave, I reserved a rental truck for a prayer, hoping I would have the money to pay for it. That Wednesday, Feb 28th, I withdrew my daughter from school and continued to pray that my income tax check would hit Friday morning, and it did.

When Friday, Mar. 2, arrived, I sprung the news on him that we were leaving, as my sister helped load most of my belongings onto a 10-foot U-Haul truck. And just like that, I left my husband and moved back to Dallas with my daughter and moved in with my Mom. The whole time I lived in Georgia, I felt like Eeyore (from Winnie the Pooh), especially when he had a gloomy rain cloud hovering over him. He once said, "Don't worry about me. Go and enjoy yourself. I'll stay here and be miserable." I always felt like that, miserable, hopeless, and dreary. But something prophetic happened as we began traveling back to Texas on a rainy and gloomy day. As soon as we crossed the Georgia state line into Alabama, the rain stopped, and as I drove I felt the weight of my own personal rain cloud leave me and the sun shone on us the whole ride home. That moment confirmed that I did the right thing. It was like God was telling me it's going to be OK. And it eventually was.

That's the CliffsNotes version of my story. So much more happened in my life that I feel could help you understand and give you insight into the craziness of toxic relationships. But the key to all this is that I would never have been able to escape had it not been for GOD. Only after trusting Him was I able to be intentional with my prayers and realize my worth. Why wasn't I able to do all of this before then? Because I made a man my idol. Everything I did or didn't do revolved around my ex. I was willing to do and sacrifice anything to keep my family together, even if it meant experiencing those dark days. At that point, I was living with fear as my master. Fear of being a single mother, fear that my future kids wouldn't have the same father, fear of getting a divorce, fear of not finding anyone else to love me. Fear was my foundation and what I had based all of my prior decisions on.

When I finally discovered I was settling out of fear and turned my situation over to God, I began to write in my journal and on any other piece of paper I could find. I read every self-help book I could find, took notes, recited affirmations, attended women's retreats, fasted, and prayed, trying to keep myself occupied and sane. But, most importantly, I made a decision. I decided to trust God and to leave my toxic environment behind, so I could not only be saved but also protect my child from pain. Certain activities and journal entries I wrote helped me acknowledge my truths and make the right decision to leave and get on the road to my healing.

See, I had to make that decision. There was not a family member or friend or book that could have told me to leave him. I had to figure out those things for myself, so I wouldn't go back. And you'll need to make that decision for yourself. That, ladies, is why I created this tool, as a guide to help you lay out the facts and make a decision, AND be OK with your decision. If you just listen to someone else, you are almost guaranteed to go back and indulge once again in a cycle of abusive behavior. That is not what the Lord intended for you; and if part of my purpose is to help you by sharing my experience, then to God be glory for using something that was meant to kill me and using it for good.

While you were reading, did you find yourself saying, "Me too"? Looking back on my situation, yes, I totally ignored any and all red flags. For instance, he had always been disrespectful before then, but after we were married it only elevated. I would either laugh it off or completely ignore it. My responses enabled him and gave him permission to continue his behavior. I also ignored all the signs and warnings from family and friends. All I wanted was my family (or my idealized version of what that meant) and I ignored every red flag in my attempt to get what I wanted. In a sense, I welcomed everything that came to me because I was willing to ignore the warnings. My consequence was God giving me everything I said I never wanted to teach me a lesson. God has a sense of humor, because now I am a single mother, divorced, and if I have kids in the future they will have a different dad — everything I said I never wanted. So, please pay attention to the red flags, trust your intuition, do not be an enabler, and don't tell God what you never want in your life!

YOUR TURN: TIME TO JOURNAL

[Using the journal pages provided, write your relationship story. Use the prompts below to help you get started.]

As we begin to look over your life, your answers to these questions will open up your suppressed memories and emotions. It's going to be hard, but reading your story and understanding how you've been affected will hopefully spark the desire in you to do what's best for you and you'll distance yourself. I hope these next activities will help you see your value. No toxic relationship is worth the pain you've been settling for.

- How did you meet? How did you feel about him in the beginning?
- What was your significant other like when you first started dating? How did you feel then? Did he make you feel special?
- Do you still feel the same? What has changed in your relationship? When did you start noticing the red flags?
- Recall a specific situation that scared you or made you wonder if you should be with him. How did you deal with that situation? Did you address it with him, with others, or did you let it slide?

- How do you feel right now about your relationship, at this moment?
- Based on the previous activity, do you think you are in a toxic relationship? Circle your answer and read it aloud.
- How does it feel to know that you are/are not?

_____

_____

_____

_____

_____

_____

_____

_____

_____

_____

_____

_____

_____

_____

_____

_____

_____

_____

_____

_____

_____

_____

_____

_____

_____

_____

_____

_____

_____

_____

_____

_____

_____

_____

_____

_____

_____

_____

Genesis 50:20 (ESV): "As for you, you meant evil against me, but God meant it for good, to bring it about that many people should be kept alive, as they are today."

3 REDEEM YOUR TIX

When you redeem tickets, you are exchanging them for something you value, right? When children go to an amusement park, they redeem their tickets for the coolest toy for the value of the tickets they won. When you go to the State Fair of Texas, you redeem your tix for rides and some of the best fried foods you've ever tasted. If you go to the movies or a concert, you redeem your tickets to experience what you hope to be one of the best, entertaining films or shows ever. Some people redeem tickets the same day they buy them or on a specific date, while some hold on to them for an extended period of time, until they feel they have built up value to get something really good. *I recently found a Dave & Buster's power card from 2010 with over 6,000 points. I have yet to redeem it.* Why? Because, girl, have you? In life, we all have been given tickets that we need to redeem. Some tickets have value that we absolutely need to hold on to, while others hold no value and merely take up space in our pockets, junk drawers, and our lives.

What are those unsalable life tickets that you have been holding on to that can be traded in for something much better? Is it stress? A toxic relationship or marriage? Emotional baggage? Self hate? Debt? Hopelessness? Financial burdens? The list goes on ... Why not redeem those useless tickets at face value, which is $0, for a better you and start collecting tickets that actually add value and peace to your life? Why do we hold on to our unprofitable life tickets and allow them to weigh us down or clutter up our lives? As women, we were created to do great things with what we are given throughout our lifetime. I've been told we all have been equipped with the tools needed to fulfill our destinies and live our best lives. It all starts with a choice, by choosing to trade in those tickets and redeem them for something of value. Trust me, it will be worth it!

Lesson: What if I told you that the longer you hold on to those valueless life tickets the less likely you are to fulfill your purpose and live the life that God has planned for you? And if you do make it happen with your worthless life tickets in hand, how long do you think you will last before those things come back around head-on and ruin you mentally in the midst of your success?

Yes, it's a process, but you first have to tell yourself that you want and deserve better. Without that mentality, you hurt your own heart. You have to pray, pray, pray, and then pray some more while asking God to reveal those worthless tickets in your life that need to be redeemed.

Prayer Jump Start: "Lord, I ask that you bless me with the gift of discernment, discernment to know who and what to release from my life. Give me discernment to release strongholds and people in my life who are blocking Your will for my life. I trust You."

Scripture: Read & Meditate

Psalm 18:1-6

1 I love you, O Lord, my strength.

2 The Lord is my rock and my fortress and my deliverer,

my God, my rock, in whom I take refuge, my shield,

and the horn of my salvation, my stronghold.

3 I call upon the Lord, who is worthy to be praised,

and I am saved from my enemies.

4 The cords of death encompassed me;

 the torrents of destruction assailed me;

5 the cords of Sheol entangled me;

 the snares of death confronted me.

6 In my distress I called upon the Lord;

to my God I cried for help.

From His temple He heard my voice,

and my cry to Him reached His ears.

Affirmation:

I AM valuable and I will only allow people in my life who will add to my worth.

I AM more than enough.

I AM not going to settle.

IS MY RELATIONSHIP VALUABLE OR WORTHLESS?

[Pros vs. Cons. List the positive and negative aspects of your relationship]

Pros (Valuable Tickets) vs. Cons (Worthless Tickets)

Pros (Valuable Tickets) vs. Cons (Worthless Tickets)

TIME TO BE HONEST: GOING DEEPER

[Based on your responses to previous activities, use the journal pages to answer the following questions.]

- Do you have more pros or cons? How does that make you feel?
- Does my relationship add value to my life or does it not hold any worth?
- Is it worth it to make it work? Why?
- Is my significant other willing to help change the cons into pros?
- If the relationship is not valuable, why are you still in the relationship? Is it out of fear? Kids?
- If you remove yourself from the toxic relationship, what would be your ideal life that you'd live?
- How does imagining that life make you feel?

_____

_____

_____

_____

_____

_____

_____

_____

_____

_____

_____

_____

_____

4 MY STORY:

JUST EXISTING IN LIFE

I think I've only admitted this verbally to my mom. But the day I got married I knew something wasn't 100%. Heck, I would even venture to say I knew it wasn't right when he asked me to marry him. Actually, let me stop: Even when we were dating, I knew it wasn't right. What I now know for a fact is that I had entered a covenant with a man with whom I wasn't *equally yoked* and was extremely broken.

I could go on, but I forgave him as I always did in our cycle of insanity. Those were all reasons to morph into Julia Roberts and become a runaway bride, but infatuation will blind you. I lived for years seeing through rose-colored glasses. True love doesn't do the things I experienced. It's true, God always offers a way for escape, but my prIde (see the "I" in the middle of the word?) wouldn't allow me to. My dad pulled me to the side 10 minutes before the wedding and told me he had all bets on me; if I wanted out, then make the call. My mom had told me, "Don't worry about anyone else. Just be sure, Destiny." My parents always warned me about him, yet they still loved us both the same when they knew we should be apart. Needless to say, my fear of being a single mom again and fear of abandonment kept me there. Yes … Again! Oh girl, didn't I tell you?

Rewind to 2008: We had broken up for the umpteenth time. Finally, two months later, I got myself settled with a new black Ford Mustang, a nice apartment, a promotion on my job — and I just found out I was 3 months pregnant with Heaven. Lucky me. I cried to my mom and grandmother and they just laughed; I was pregnant. I called him and told him I was pregnant, then sent him a pic of the positive test. (Thank God for camera phones, right?) He said, … "So," and that he was tired and would call me back. He hung up the phone. My stomach sank into my back and I cried for days. We were only dating on and off at this point and the fact that he reacted like this should have been another major red flag for me.

Eventually, he came around, but I began to turn into that desperate being I would become. A desperate woman yearning for love and for someone to be there for me. He lived out of state, in Georgia, and I was still in Texas. I know it's a lot of back and forth, but stick with me.

I went through nine months of pregnancy, without him. Instead, my mom and my sister stepped in and helped me throughout my pregnancy. Every appointment and shopping trip, I did alone or with my mom. I wasn't due for another two weeks or so when my mom came into my bedroom. Pause: After six months of living in my new apartment, I decided that it would be best to move in with my mom since I could have the support I needed. Press play: I had a temperature of 103. She and my sister rushed me to the hospital where they informed my mom that I had preeclampsia. The doctor would have to induce me or there was a risk that both my child and I would die.

By this time, I was fed up with my ex's childish ways so I didn't even bother calling him. But that didn't stop my big-head little sister from calling him and suggesting he get on the first flight out to capture the birth of his daughter. As I write this, it tires me to relive it all, but let me just say he showed up, trying to feed me ice chips and calling me "baby."

The nutshell story went like this: I gave birth. He told me to put him down to pay child support, then resented me for it. He went to prison for about a year on drug charges. I was lonely, so when he got out, we got back together, he proposed, and fast forward to me standing at the altar. I don't recall what my cousin the pastor said because I was not present at all. After we said "I do," I looked at the people in attendance, or lack thereof, and despite my apprehensions, I put on the face of enjoying our honeymoon in New Orleans, the same city where we met. Afterward, I prepared to move to his hometown of Atlanta. I was leaving behind a great job, my family, and friends — with our daughter in tow.

Then, red flag, I drove while he rode shotgun for 12 hours, never once offering to drive. We headed to our newly leased home in Palmetto, Georgia, in a raggedy U-haul truck. Palmetto is a small country town about 25 miles south of Atlanta. A three-bedroom, 2.5 bathroom house on a quiet street was a dream come true. It seemed all of the arguing and begging him to grow up had finally paid off. I did it! I changed him. And they said it couldn't be done! He had put us up in a nice home. Though we didn't have much in regards to furniture, I brought a little bit of furniture from Texas. Heaven's room was fully furnished and that is all that mattered to me. We were finally a family. We were beginning our life together. We had dinner as a family nightly. My God,

I was all smiles and things were perfect for the first month and a half. Too perfect, now that I look back.

Equally Yoked Explained: Growing up, I would always hear the saying about being "equally yoked," but I never understood what it meant. So now that I get it, let me break it down for you. The term "equally yoked" comes from a time when farmers would yoke two animals together to plow the land. A yoke is a wooden cross piece that fits over the shoulders of the animals to connect them to the plow or cart that they need to pull. Farmers would choose two oxen that were equal in weight and stature so that they could uniformly share the pressure of work. You can imagine if an ox that was small and bony was paired with a large and strong ox, the smaller ox would leave the majority of the responsibility and pressure on the larger ox. The smaller ox is unable to match the ability to work as hard or carry as much weight as the larger ox. As a result, the larger ox would be worn down easier, exerting too much effort to handle all of the responsibility that was created for two oxen, not just one. Get it? If we were to apply this to life, it looks like single mothers or fathers doing it all alone or one person trying to make a relationship work, or *you* trying to make a relationship work with someone who is not on the same level as you. If you settle for someone who is not as strong, mentally stable, or who doesn't hold the same desire to put effort in your relationship, then you will always be doing most of the work in the relationship. The relationship will burn out much faster because the person you are with either does not have the capability to operate on the same level as you or just doesn't have the desire to.

Lesson: Close your eyes and imagine yourself purposely stepping outside of your home and into a tornado. The wind sharply pierces your face and body. You can barely keep your eyes open because the wind is so strong that it burns your eyes. Debris is flying everywhere, so you duck and dodge it all. Your body is weighed down because you are afraid to fight the storm. So you just stand still, thinking if you don't fight it that it won't hurt as bad and eventually the storm will pass. Maybe true, but why wait? Learn the pattern of the storm. Be as a palm tree and learn to bend with it. Endure the pain, tell yourself you can get through, trust the Lord to get you there, and then start moving, taking one step forward at a time. Widen your stance, bend down, don't allow that storm to push you backward. But if it does, remember that only helps you gain traction. Keep moving. If you must crawl your way out, then get low and weather the storm. Don't allow it to take anymore pain from you, don't allow it to beat you down. Do your part and trust God to calm your storm. Whatever it is that's beating you down, fight through the storm and it will be fine.

Prayer Jump Start: "Lord, calm the storms in my life and give me strength to endure until they cease. Equip me with the technique and provisions I need to weather the storms in my life."

Scripture: Read & Meditate

Psalm 107:29-31 (KJV)

29 He maketh the storm a calm,

so that the waves thereof are still.

30 Then are they glad because they be quiet;

so He bringeth them unto their desired haven.

31 Oh that men would praise the Lord for his goodness, and for his wonderful works to the children of men!

Affirmation:

I AM more than a conqueror and I can weather any storm.

I AM stronger than my current situation.

I AM fearless.

TIME TO BE HONEST: GAINS & LOSSES?

[List the major concerns you have about staying in your relationship.

Do the same for leaving. Do you have a lot to lose or gain if you stay?

And if you leave?]

GAINS

Stay:

_____

_____

_____

_____

_____

_____

_____

_____

Leave:
_____

_____

_____

_____

_____

LOSSES

Stay:
_____

_____

_____

_____

_____

_____

Leave:
_____

_____

_____

_____

_____

_____

_____

- Do you have a lot to lose or gain if you stay?
- Do you have a lot to lose or gain if you leave?
- Are the gains or losses worth keeping the toxicity in your life?

The answers to these questions will open the thoughts that you may experience about your relationship and whether you feel like you are the one losing because you choose to leave. You also will see if you have everything to gain from your exit.

_____

_____

_____

_____

_____

_____

_____

_____

_____

_____

_____

_____

_____

_____

5 BEYOND THE CLOUDS:

DEVELOPING PERSPECTIVE

In 2016, I sat on a plane from NYC contemplating my life. For me, it was the lowest point in my life. I had been jobless for over a year, my husband at that time was in jail, I had no money to my name and was recovering from bankruptcy. At that point, I hadn't finished college and was chasing my dream of becoming an actress. But I had this weird sense of peace, a peace that everything would be OK, even though my mind would get the best of me and I would stress. I was planning to read "The Power of the Actor" by Ivana Chubbuck, but instead I felt the urge to type. This is what I wrote:

As I look out the window and down at the earth, I see the past and how small it looks in comparison to the beautiful view I have from above. I see the sun-kissed clouds that cover that past and allow me to see a beautiful picture above it all. I am so close. See, where I am now is waiting, somewhere between the clouds and the heavens waiting in line for my breakthrough from the heavens. I am so close to God that when the sky opens and begins to pour out my blessings, I'll be able to feel it and catch it before the clouds and the earth can soak it up.

When the clouds pass and I can see the ground from 30,000 feet, it all looks like a puzzle of a million different shapes perfectly placed on the ground. Each piece represents a part of my life that I have encountered up to now and the shape of this amazing body of land we call life.

I don't understand why some parts are filled with water, some grass, some light, some dark, some other specks, some covered with clouds, but I know the photo it makes when you take a step back, rise above, and look down on everything it took to make it. It's worth it, breathtaking, serene, and worth it. God said He would not forsake you in your times of trouble and that if He made a promise, though it may tarry, it shall surely come.

Don't be afraid to look at your life from this perspective. Far too often, the enemy places your problems within plain sight and tries to blind you with it. You forget about your ability to step back and see the big picture and that every trial is a perfectly placed piece of a puzzle that represents your life and is needed to form your earth. The clouds are simply God covering your pieces of land when you need it the most. Rise above it all and see how beautiful your pieces of land really are and prepare for it to rain blessings.

Written by: Destiny in August of 2016

Lesson: I was drinking a glass of tea one morning when I thought of how pain is similar to a tea bag. Let me explain. In order for a tea bag to be of any use, it has to steep in water. You will not truly enjoy the tea unless it is mixed with its partner, water. A tea bag has to soak in order to turn the water and give it color, fragrance, and flavor.

If you look at it from life's perspective, then we are the water and the tea bag is the pain that we have endured. If it soaks long enough, pain will take our plain water and give us a new color and identity. Once you add the tea bag to the water, you can't reverse it. The tea bag will leave some color and flavor in the water. So, when pain enters your life, it's going to leave its traces behind. Just like tea, it cannot be reversed. We can't go back to who we were before the decisions we made, what we accepted, what we settled for, etc. We are forever changed by the pain.

The only element the tea bag cannot provide you is a sweetener. You have to add that yourself. You have to make a choice and decide how much sweetener you want to add, whether you want bitter tea or sweet tea. Sweetener is our perspective. We can make it sweet with a positive perspective and make a choice that despite the pain we will be better or we can only add a tiny bit of sweetener and keep our tea bitter. Which will make it harder to enjoy your tea, your life. What do you think? Are you going to keep your tea bitter or add sweetener?

Prayer Jump Start: "Lord, no matter what life I have lived before this moment. No matter how much pain I endured, or how hurt and angry I may be, I ask that You heal my heart. Change my heart, heal it, and give me a positive perspective. Lord, I want to be better, not bitter."

Scripture: Read & Meditate

Psalm 147:3 (ESV)

He heals the brokenhearted

And binds up their wounds.

Affirmation:

I AM healed.

I AM enough.

I AM taking it one day at a time.

I AM positive.

6 ACCEPTING MY TRUTH

I had to make a decision about my toxic situation and whether I was going to save not only myself but my child from any more pain. So, I LEFT. I left because I was being abused mentally, emotionally, and even physically a few times. The fact that I fought back or we made up didn't justify anything. I left because I had to or my child would grow up in a horribly toxic environment and as her mother it is my duty to protect her. Living under these conditions was making me feel as though my soul was being sucked from me.

At this moment, as I am completing this journal almost five years after the moment God prompted me to write my story, it finally clicked. He actually grabbed a gun to ... kill me. Not to scare me, but to kill me. Why else would he grab a firearm and aim it at my head? I wasn't a threat, there was no cause for self-defense. It had to go through his mind, the mind of the man who I married, to physically get a loaded gun and shoot me. I never thought about that until June 16, 2021, as I write this, that he was filled with intention to shoot me.

I am in disbelief even now. God spared me that night. He froze time and removed all fear, calmed me despite the fact I had a gun pointed at me. And when I looked at myself in that mirror, He showed me that spiritually my soul, who I was, was being stripped from me. If I had stayed, I would forever be lost in the darkness never to return and would have risked becoming not only unrecognizable to God, but to myself. The flame of the candle that burned in me, that burns inside us all, was dimming and was only one short breath away from being snuffed out forever. That was the exact moment when I was Inspired to Live Again.

I had come to that fork in the road and I had begun to seek change. There was not a family member, friend, or book that could have influenced me at that point. I had to do this on my own, make the decision to stay or leave. I had to figure it out for myself, so I knew I wouldn't go back. And now, ladies, it's time for you to make your decision. Taking a magnifying glass and picking apart my circumstances and relationship and creating painfully honest journal entries helped me acknowledge my truths and make the right decision for me and my daughter.

Use this guide to help you lay out the facts of your own situation, and to decide what's truly best for you. *Be at peace with your decision.* If you just listen to someone else's advice, you are almost guaranteed to go back and once again indulge in a cycle of abusive behavior. That is not what the Lord intended for you and why I choose to be transparent about my experience with toxic relationships. I believe we go through certain experiences to learn a lesson, for both ourselves and for others.

James 1:5 (ESV): "If any of you lacks wisdom, let him ask God, who gives generously to all without reproach, and it will be given him."

TIME TO BE HONEST: MAKE A DECISION

[Use the space below to answer the following questions.]

- What are you going to do: keep trying or leave?
- What's making you stay?
- What compels you to leave?
- What is your decision based on?
- If you are choosing to stay, do you trust that proper changes can be made?
- If you are choosing to leave, are you at peace with your decision?
- Are you ready to Live Again?

Doubting your decision, missing him, and wanting to go back to the familiar chaos are all part of the process. But every time you have thoughts that make you wonder if you made the wrong decision, I want you to open up this workbook and reread your answers, because that is your truth! Even if you have to do it a million times a day, embrace your decision and keep taking it one day at a time.

spired To Live Again

SETTING A DATE

[Write it in the circle below.]

If you choose to stay and keep trying, set a date. A date that you keep to yourself. A date if he has not done his part and gotten help or done whatever he has agreed to do. If he meets the deadline, great! Maybe there is hope. If he does not, don't keep moving the date; be firm in your decision.

If you choose to leave, set a date. A date that you will be gone by. You are going to need a quick and safe exit plan that you can execute easily and under the radar.

Now, it's time to go into prayer about your dates and/or exit strategy.

Note: If you fear for your life, DON'T WAIT! DO NOT BE AFRAID TO CALL 911 or go to the police station and ask for an escort to protect you as you leave.

Most importantly, once you leave: **Do Not Look Back.**

7 ROAD TO HEALING:

IS THIS MY FAULT?

I struggled with guilt, wondering if this is all my fault. And you may be experiencing it too. The short answer is "No," it was not all my fault, and neither is it all yours. Notice, I said all. The detailed answer is that while we aren't the person who was to blame in the toxic relationship, we do have to claim partial responsibility. You are probably thinking, "What is she talking about? I am not to blame for his lack of self-control and narcissistic ways." I will agree 100%. But we have to own the fact that we ignored the warnings of friends and family, we looked past the red flags, and we in some way enabled him and his ways and didn't set any boundaries. Doing that gave him the power and the belief that he could do and say anything that he wanted to you because he knew you weren't going to do anything about it.

I never expected to accept this until one day of self-reflecting and trying to figure out how I let this go on for so long and how I had let something so wrong feel so normal to me. That's when I figured out that all I had to do was say, "No." If only I had set boundaries, stood up for myself, let my "no" mean "no," took into consideration what everyone was saying about him, ran at the first sight of red flags, and established a list of nonnegotiables for all relationships … then this could have gone totally different. The fact remains, it didn't. I'm willing to bet that you, like I, lacked value and/or identity so it made it that much easier for him to take advantage of you. You need to be accountable because you, like him, had a choice. That's it. Acknowledging the part you played in this situation will help build you up emotionally so that in any future relationships you will know what not to do while also setting your boundaries. You can't fix or keep from repeating what you don't know.

James 5:16 (ESV): "Therefore, confess your sins to one another and pray for one another, that you may be healed. The prayer of a righteous person has great power as it is working."

75

OWNING YOUR CHOICES

[Write down a list of things you take ownership for and things you could have done differently, but didn't. Once you've done that, list the results or consequences you experienced.]

I TAKE OWNERSHIP FOR ...

AS A RESULT OF MY DECISIONS, I EXPERIENCED ...

NONNEGOTIABLES

[Use your answers from the previous charts to help you list your nonnegotiables.]

What is a nonnegotiable? It is a set of values or principles that you have in common in a relationship. These are things that you refuse to settle on because they are a priority to you and will aid in making the relationship work. For example: You may require that he must be a man of integrity, so you know that he is trustworthy or you may require that he is supportive or passionate about his dreams/goals and yours.

The spectrum on your list may be broad, but I want to get your mind thinking forward about what you are willing and unwilling to accept.

MY NONNEGOTIABLES FOR ANY
FUTURE RELATIONSHIPS ARE...

ASK FOR HELP

I navigated most of the situation and road to healing alone. I do not want that for you. That road was lonely and would have been a bit easier if I had someone to call on. So, I suggest that you find someone to lean on, to be your accountability partner, and to hold your hand throughout this process. Not someone who just wants to be in your business, not someone who doesn't have your best interest at heart, not someone connected to your abuser. Yes, abuser. Much of what we covered thus far is a form of abuse. You need someone who will allow you to vent judgment-free without offering their opinion. You need to vent out loud and on paper. Find someone who tells it like it is, who is brutally honest, and is a great listener. You may not want to hear this but you need it. You need a friend who, most importantly, will love you just as much in the state that you are in.

LET'S BE HONEST: WHO CAN I COUNT ON?

[Use the journal to help you answer the following questions.]

- Who do you know who isn't biased about your relationship?
- Who warned you about your relationship before things took that toxic turn?

Pray about it and ask God for discernment in who you can lean on.

_____

_____

_____

_____

_____

_____

_____

_____

WHO IS MY ACCOUNTABILITY PARTNER?

(For this activity, write down the names of three people you trust and then answer the following about each person.)

Person #1_____

Things you like about this person:

_____

_____

_____

_____

_____

_____

_____

_____

_____

_____

Things you dislike about this person:

_____

_____

_____

_____

_____

_____

_____

_____

_____

_____

_____

_____

What makes them trustworthy?

_____

_____

_____

_____

_____

_____

_____

_____

_____

Have they ever told a secret? If so, were you upset?

_____

_____

_____

_____

_____

_____

_____

_____

_____

_____

_____

_____

If you tell them something, do they listen?

_____

_____

_____

_____

_____

_____

_____

_____

_____

Do they lift you up when you are down?

_____

_____

_____

_____

_____

_____

_____

_____

_____

_____

_____

Person #2_____

Things you like about this person:

_____

_____

_____

_____

_____

_____

_____

_____

_____

_____

Things you dislike about this person:

_____

_____

_____

_____

_____

_____

_____

_____

_____

_____

What makes them trustworthy?

_____

_____

_____

_____

_____

_____

_____

Have they ever told a secret? If so, were you upset?

_____

_____

_____

_____

_____

_____

_____

_____

_____

_____

_____

_____

If you tell them something, do they listen?

_____

_____

_____

_____

_____

_____

_____

_____

_____

_____

_____

_____

_____

Do they lift you up when you are down?

_____

_____

_____

_____

_____

_____

_____

_____

_____

_____

Person #3_____

Things you like about this person:

_____

_____

_____

_____

_____

_____

_____

_____

_____

_____

_____

Things you dislike about this person:

_____

_____

_____

_____

_____

_____

_____

_____

_____

What makes them trustworthy?

_____

_____

_____

_____

_____

_____

_____

_____

_____

_____

_____

_____

_____

_____

Have they ever told a secret? If so, were you upset?

_____

_____

_____

_____

_____

_____

_____

_____

_____

If you tell them something, do they listen?

_____

_____

_____

_____

_____

_____

_____

_____

_____

_____

_____

_____

Do they lift you up when you are down?

Who do you think will be the best person to choose to be your accountability partner? (Circle one)

Person 1   **Person 2**   **Person 3**

Now, it's time to call the person you chose or meet them face to face. Share as much as you want or share very little and gauge their interest in being your accountability partner. Do not worry if you haven't found the right partner. Keep listening to God and He will send the right person. Be very selective of who you share your personal information with, and don't feel obligated to tell anyone the details until you are ready. That is 100% your right!

- How did the call/meet go?
- Do you feel like you made the right choice?
- Did you feel judged?
- How do you feel after the call/meet ended?
- Do you feel at peace? Why or why not?

_____

_____

_____

_____

_____

_____
_____
_____
_____
_____
_____
_____
_____
_____
_____
_____
_____
_____
_____
_____
_____
_____
_____
_____
_____
_____
_____
_____
_____
_____
_____
_____
_____

8 GUILT TRIP

I'd be lying if I said that during the duration of our on-and-off-again relationship I didn't take him back every time. Of course I did. I was caught up in the never-ending cycle of toxicity that always draws you back. I thought everything was going to be smooth sailing because I had finally broken the cycle when I left for the final time! I mean, I was ready to move on and begin healing! But I wasn't prepared for the depression, anxiety, and irritability, combined with the guilt, shame, fear, and thoughts of what if I would have just stayed.

No one ever tells you that once you decide to leave a toxic relationship that you sometimes feel bad for deciding to put yourself first. The way that you feel is like a Relationship PTSD. Post-Traumatic Stress Disorder. Who would have thought you would have something in common with war veterans? Relationship PTSD is basically an extreme anxiety disorder that's usually caused by a traumatic and/or life-threatening experience. What you experience in a toxic relationship can be traumatic, and traumatic events always take a toll on us in some way, shape, or form. The longer you stay stuck in your cycle of toxicity, the longer it may take to heal. And if you're considering going back to the relationship that has given you so much pain, please, remember this: The person who hurt you can't be the person to heal you. The healing starts alone. At this point in your journey, you have to see the light and the better days ahead of you. They are possible! You have to be filled with hope and know that on the other side of this pain is healing and on the other side of healing is PURE JOY!

I asked a friend of mine, Nicole, who will forever hold a place in my heart, to write something to inspire you and give you hope to travel to the other side of healing. It definitely hits us differently when you have multiple people sharing testimonies with the same underlying theme. I asked her to share her story to help you to understand you are not alone — not now and not in any part of this process of discovering your truth and healing.

As you read her story below, make note of how God moved strategically throughout her story. He is doing the same for you. You are reading this journal aren't you? (wink)

NICOLE'S STORY

I met my husband when I was 23 years old and struggling to get out of a physically abusive relationship. He was my knight in shining armor. He helped me escape. However, my wonderful dream slowly deteriorated and went from being a bad dream to a nightmare.

First, it was just little things. He was not much of a gentleman. He was inconsiderate and rude to me. By the time I realized what a jerk he was, I was already pregnant and felt like I had nowhere to go. I moved in with him and things got worse. We were always broke. He began to disappear in the middle of the night and would get furious if I questioned him about it. I never got to meet any of his friends and we never went anywhere together. I mean, we were rarely ever even home together.

I had gathered that he was out smoking pot with his friends. We fought about it, often. But everyone told me it was "just pot" so I was overreacting. I eventually learned that it was not pot at all. He was actually doing meth. I later found out he was dealing pot (out of our house!) to pay for his meth addiction. It took me 3-1/2years to put this all together.

So, after almost four years, I finally got enough courage to leave him and take our 3-year-old daughter. I settled into a new life and was doing great on my own being a single mom. I had started dating a new guy who totally adored me. Then one year later almost to the day, I saw my ex at a party. I got drunk and slept with him. I ended up getting pregnant again. He swore he had changed. He said he missed me and wanted to be a family. So, I took him back. I truly felt like I had no choice. I was not prepared to be a single mom of two children. I very quickly realized he had not changed. But I found out I was about to have a special needs child and I was terrified. So I stayed and just tried to ignore his behavior. He never physically hit me, so I always thought it was still better than my past relationship.

Mother's Day weekend 2017. I had the worst case of the flu I have ever had. I was home in bed; my husband was out on another bender. I had not seen him in a couple days. At 3 p.m. I got a phone call from a police officer in Dallas saying my husband had been arrested. He had been pulled over for road rage. Turned out he was high and had enough meth on him to be charged for distribution. I was actually so relieved!

I thought maybe, just maybe, this would be his wake-up call. I had planned to leave him in jail to sober up and hopefully learn his lesson. His mother had other plans. She bailed him out and just like that he was home.

When he got home, I finally stood up to him and gave him an ultimatum. Clean up or I was taking the girls and leaving. I took him straight to rehab that night. I spent both of my daughters' entire college funds to get him in. He stayed for 30 days. His new sobriety lasted less than a month. When he slipped, it wasn't so much that he slipped but that he couldn't care less that he did. He lied about it. He continued to lie and quickly fell back into his old habits.

In December 2017, I met a lady who totally changed my life while on a weekend trip that turned my world around. Of all places, a Girl Scouts camping trip! A God-ordained camping trip. I rode out with a total stranger. She was a new mom in our troop. I truly believe God put me in that car with her. I am not sure how we started talking about such personal things, but she was recently out of a toxic relationship and she helped me realize how toxic my own relationship was. I told her everything that had happened over the past six months in my relationship. She gave me some great advice and helped me realize I had every right to leave my husband. I needed confirmation. That is what she gave me.

After that weekend, I had the strength to finally do it. When I got home, I started planning how to actually leave him. I kept my mouth shut and kept planning. On Christmas night, he tried to leave to go get high. I had enough. I finally told him I was DONE and leaving. I told him I was leaving in two weeks. Things got very ugly so I moved up my exit to that weekend.

Things were extremely hard for the first year after I left. He was angry and mean. He was high every time we saw him for our court-appointed visitations. He did everything he could to make my life a living hell. He didn't care if he hurt our girls as long as he hurt me. It was so hard to see what this was doing to my babies. Most of the time I felt guilty. I felt like I should have stayed so my girls would not have to endure this. Eventually, he got clean and his anger subsided. He now has his visitation reinstated. We still don't exactly get along but we are cordial for our girls.

Fast forward three years. I have a great job and just bought my first house. And through all that darkness, now I am happy. Truly happy. The best part is, I did it all on my own!

- Nicole C.

IG:@Nicolecox9559

Revelation 21:4 (ESV): "He will wipe away every tear from their eyes, and death shall be no more, neither shall there be mourning, nor crying, nor pain anymore, for the former things have passed away."

9 TAKE NOTES

It helped me tremendously to write out my thoughts and prayers, because in the state of mind I was in, my life seemed like the back of a tapestry — everything was confusing and chaotic on one side, but I was hopeful and knew that eventually on the other side of this was a beautiful, strategically custom-designed tapestry. I was determined to see the beautiful outcome of my decision, so I journaled daily. I realized when I had all of my information and inspiration in one place, it became easier to reflect on. For that reason, after the guided journal portion, I have included a full 200-page journal for you to write down your own journey. When complete, you will have your transformation written out for you to look back on and thank God that you aren't where you used to be.

TIME TO BE HONEST: JOURNALING

- How does it make you feel to see your life and thoughts written out on paper?
- Are you being honest about everything you have written thus far? If not, why not?

10 PRAYER & FASTING

Prayer and seeking God helped me heal when I finally understood the POWER of prayer and saw it beginning to work with my own eyes. I was in a desperate place when I began to seek God's presence. I knew from how I was raised that I had to lean on Him. So, I put on my armor and I went to war. My whole house was my war room. I would sit at the table reading the Word and then work my way through my house, starting in the kitchen and ending in my daughter's room, covering my home and family in prayer. I also remember my first petition to God after I felt it was time to leave my toxic marriage. I prayed and asked that He not keep me broken, but instead make me better and not bitter. And He has done just that. That simple, heartfelt prayer is what sustains me even now.

Many people ask why I don't seem broken or hate my ex. Here is the thing: I don't know. The only thing I can do is give God the glory. Why? Because ever since I prayed that prayer, my heart has held some sort of peace about my past trauma. If it worked for me, then I'm sure it's possible for you too. Just pray a prayer similar to this:

"Lord, thank You for this day. Thank You in advance for making provisions for all that I will need this week. Give me strength to smile and see life from Your perspective as I heal. I speak into existence a blessed week! I speak healing over my life and the lives of others. I declare Your favor over my life and decree that any brokenness in my heart will be healed.

In Jesus' name … AMEN"

Fasting was necessary for me also. Why? For me, fasting gave me clarity and I felt like I could hear God clearly. Fasting also, because I was so hungry (lol), kept me closer to God. I felt like I had to pray for Him to give me strength to keep going. Fasting is a sacrifice and forces you to lean on God. While fasting doesn't force God's hand, it's as if saying, "Lord, I need You more than the things I love." See, fasting can be from social media, foods, etc. It's denying yourself the things in which you find pleasure. Some things only happen via prayer and fasting.

11 POSITIVE AFFIRMATIONS:

THE POWER OF I AM

On my journey, I discovered the power of positive affirmations. These positive statements help keep you from doubting yourself and erase any negative thoughts. I fell in love with these I AM's. I and AM when used together are two of the most powerful words, so much so that you begin to call forth and manifest whatever follows I AM. The words I AM appear more than 300 times in the Bible, mainly used by Jesus. "I AM the Alpha and the Omega" (Revelation 1:8), "I AM the bread of life" (John 6:35), "I AM the light of the world" (John 8:12), are just a few that He used. Whatever follows the words "I AM" is His truth. We have the power to call those things that are not as though they were (Romans 4:17). That means we have been given the power to speak things into existence through the power of the tongue, manifesting whatever we speak. Using I AM's daily overpowered my negative self-talk and my habit of self-sabotage and placed me in a positive and healthy mindset. I looked in the mirror daily and told myself how amazing I was, even if I didn't feel amazing at that point in time. You can use I AM's to help you remember that you are valuable and worthy of living out your fullest life.

I have listed a few I AM's that you should tell yourself daily. There's also space for you to create your own.

I AM

I AM ... BEAUTIFUL

I AM ...WORTHY

I AM ... LOVED

I AM ... STRONG

I AM ... ABLE

I AM ... VALUABLE

I AM ... AT PEACE

I AM ... HEALED

I AM ... FULL OF JOY

I AM ...

I AM ...

I AM ...

I AM ...

I AM ...

I AM ...

I AM ...

I AM ...

I AM ...

I AM ...

I AM ...

I AM ...

I AM ...

I AM ...

I AM ...

I AM ...

I AM ...

I AM ...

I AM ...

I AM ...

I AM ...

I AM ...

I AM ...

I AM ...

I AM ...

I AM ...

I AM ...

I AM …

I AM …

I AM …

I AM …

I AM …

I AM …

I AM …

I AM …

I AM …

I AM …

I AM …

I AM …

I AM …

I AM …

I AM …

12 IT'S TIME TO LIVE AGAIN

I totally believe it's possible that I was the right woman for the wrong man.

As you read, I was in and out of an unhealthy relationship. I won't say I wasted my time, because out of something so toxic came something so Heavenly. I endured pain, hurt, abuse, depression, stress, and more. I allowed my love for someone who couldn't see past the box he lived in to halt my progression, to cloud my thinking, and hold me hostage mentally. I allowed my mind to be so into my relationship and "playing house" before we even got married instead of where it should have been ... on seeking God first. And because I let it all consume me, I felt lost, had no peace, and I was in a constant state of fear, worry, and anxiety. I'm sure many of you feel or have felt the same way at some point in your life. I'll admit it took me awhile to finally get the nerve and desire to want to let it go. We all do it. We all have wanted to hold on to life tickets that were no good and without value because we feel things will eventually change or we think we can change them. I had to learn that there is a difference between quitting and letting go — especially if you have given it your all to try to make it work. I guess you can say that after much pain, I finally redeemed my ticket. I am Living Again.

7 STEPS TO LIVING AGAIN

There's a critical point in time when a woman decides to leave a toxic relationship and is left only with her thoughts. That's where the cycle either repeats itself or she is inspired to find a way out. This guide can be used either after leaving a toxic relationship to help you move on from the cycle of pain or inspire those of you who are currently in toxic relationships to decide to no longer settle but to Live Again!

My hope is to inspire every woman to no longer settle in the toxicity but help you to understand that you deserve to live your purpose and achieve an abundant life. In order for the cycle not to repeat itself, you have to take the necessary steps to move forward into the unknown. I compiled a few steps that I took that helped me to move forward and not go back to the person who was the cause of my pain.

[Review these steps and place a check next to the ones you have done.]

- **Make a decision.** I let my "yes" be "yes" and my "no" be "no." A lot of times we go back and forth and it keeps us in a constant state of confusion. Making a decision is one of the first steps to jump on the road to healing.

- **Set a date.** I wrote down goal dates. I gave myself a deadline for him, and if he hadn't sought out help by that date, then I knew I would have to push forward with my exit plan. For some of you in violent situations, this may not be an option; you need to move forward with creating a safe exit plan.

- **Create an exit plan.** Pray about it, listen, write it down, and execute. God always gives you a way to escape.

- **Ask for help.** I didn't really have anyone I wanted to discuss my situation with, but when I knew it was time to leave, I called on my sister to be there with me the day I moved out. She was there for me for my safety and with no questions asked. Find someone you trust to be there for you

- **Take notes.** Every sermon or word of encouragement that inspired me, I kept. I have countless notebooks and sticky notes with scriptures and notes I wrote down. At times, YOU are the only encouragement that you will have access to.

- **Pray and fast.** I prayed and fasted for my mind, for clarity, and for peace about the decision I was making. What you are doing will change your life and so will prayer and fasting.

- **Live Again!** I decided that I would not let my decision to leave a toxic marriage and what I experienced make me bitter. Instead, I chose to be a better woman, to heal, to be the best version of myself and live again. Les Brown has a saying: "Live Full and Die Empty." I hope that you choose that too.

I wrote the following to be transparent, obedient, and give hope to someone who needs it. You are not the only person this has happened to. And you are not alone.

YES, I DID!

YES, I'M DIVORCED

YES, I WAS EMBARRASSED

YES, I WAS DEPRESSED

YES, I WAS WORRIED ABOUT OTHER PEOPLE'S OPINIONS

YES, IT WAS A LESSON LEARNED

YES, IT WAS TOXIC

YES, THERE WERE SIGNS

YES, I IGNORED THEM

but...

YES, I MADE THE RIGHT DECISION AND LEFT

YES, GOD MOVED THAT MOUNTAIN

YES, I'M FULL OF JOY

YES, I GOT MY GLOW BACK

YES, I'M COMING FOR WHAT'S MINE

YES, THE LORD WAS, IS, AND WILL ALWAYS BE MY STRENGTH

and...

NOPE, I DON'T HAVE ANY REGRETS

AM I GOING TO OFFICIALLY CELEBRATE THE END OF THE DARKEST YEARS OF MY LIFE AND STEP INTO THIS NEW CHAPTER WITH GRACE AND CONFIDENCE?

ABSOLUTELY!

We all go through trials and disappointments, but the key is to figure out what the purpose was in it all. Times may get dark and you can't see a way out, but if you let your light shine through the darkness it has no choice but to FLEE. LIGHT is more POWERFUL than darkness.

John 1:5 (ESV): "The light shines in the darkness, and the darkness has not overcome it."

13 FACTS OVER FEELINGS

Now that you've written out your truth, go back and read your answers as many times as you need in order to stay rooted in your truth. Through my own experience, I learned that when we are in life-altering relationships with loved ones we must remember the facts because our hearts and our eyes, unintentionally sometimes, lie to us and lead us astray.

FACTS OVER FEELINGS!

JOURNAL
TO HEAL...
HEAL TO ...
Live Again

Inspired To Live Again

Inspired To Live Again

175

_____

_____

_____

_____

_____

_____

_____

_____

_____

_____

_____

_____

_____

_____

_____

_____

_____

_____

_____

_____

_____

_____

_____

_____

_____

_____

_____

_____

_____

_____

_____

_____

_____

_____

_____

_____

_____

_____

_____

_____

_____

_____

_____

_____

_____

_____

_____

_____

_____

_____

_____

_____

_____

_____

_____

_____

_____

_____

_____

_____

_____

_____

_____

_____

_____

_____

_____

_____

_____

_____

_____

_____

_____

_____

_____

_____

_____

_____

_____

_____

_____

_____

_____

_____

_____

_____

_____

_____

_____

_____

_____

_____

_____

_____

_____

_____

_____

_____

_____

_____

_____

_____

_____

_____

_____

_____

_____

_____

_____

ABOUT THE AUTHOR

Some situations in life catch us off guard and turn our life upside down. Mine was a toxic relationship. I would have never predicted that I would endure such pain and heartache. I would have never thought that the man I genuinely loved would at some point look at me as his enemy and break me down almost to the point of no return. BUT GOD and my desire to want to live my best life and not let the pain inflicted on me make me bitter, helped me to overcome. I am a survivor and I wanted to share how God took a bad situation and turned it around and used it for my good.

I didn't want to just write a boring book telling my personal business, but I did want my personal experience to serve a purpose. So, I created a tool that I pray will help women discover their worth and begin the journey to healing, a proven tool that worked for me. So if only one person benefits from this journal and applies it then that's a win in my eyes. A win for God, who was my ultimate reference not only to write this book but a reference I leaned completely on to grow through my situation. I wanted to know that what I went through was for a purpose. That purpose is to… **INSPIRE WOMEN TO LIVE AGAIN.**

Destiny Washington is an actress, owner of TAPED Studios, and Mom to an amazing daughter. She currently resides in Dallas, Texas.

Connect with me and share your story!

WWW.DESTINYWASHINGTON.COM

Inspired2LiveAgain@gmail.com

@IamDestinyWashington

Made in the USA
Middletown, DE
30 September 2021